Understanding Addiction and Treatment

For more information or

to get help for a suffering addict, visit

www.lakesidemilam.com or call 1-800-232-1559.

Introduction

Over 25 years ago a small group of people moved to establish a treatment system for alcoholics and addicts informed by the research and experience of Dr. James Milam, outlined in his landmark book *Under the Influence*. The goal was to build an effective, affordable treatment network that addressed the needs of each patient from detoxification to inpatient and outpatient treatment to a then much neglected regimen of continuing care after primary treatment. A quarter of a century later Lakeside-Milam Recovery Centers, as it is now known, has treated over 100,000 patients in an adult inpatient center, an adolescent inpatient center, and eleven outpatient centers around Puget Sound. While science has discovered a great deal about the nature of chemical addiction in that time, all of the latest findings support the essence of Dr. Milam's work published over 27 years ago: That alcoholism/addiction is a treatable physiological disease, that there exists a well marked path to recovery and that involvement in 12-step programs plays a crucial role in the recovery of the addicted person.

In *Under the Influence,* Dr. Milam provided a wealth of information on the nature of alcohol, its effects on the human body and brain, and the development and progression of the disease of addiction. With the available research, he speculated on the causes of the disease while outlining a course of treatment that has been followed by thousands of treatment programs including Lakeside-Milam Recovery Centers.

Since 1981 new research from a variety of sources has unlocked the specific origins of addiction while confirming Dr. Milam's assertion that the disease was treatable, but that alcoholics could never be "cured" to drink safely. That new research also investigated other psychoactive drugs like cocaine and heroin and arrived at the same conclusions – alcohol and drug addicts are no more responsible for becoming sick than diabetics are for contracting diabetes. Genetics rather than willpower determines who can use alcohol safely and who can't.

This booklet is intended to summarize the advances made in addiction research while reaffirming the path to recovery laid out by Dr. Milam. It touches on all drugs of addiction and explains other difficult issues such as how relapse occurs and how long treatment should last for recovery to take hold. It could not have been written had not Dr. Milam made his initial investigation into the disease. For his genius and commitment we remain forever grateful.

The Elephant and the Blind Men

Once an elephant came to a small town. People had read and heard of elephants but no one in the town had ever seen one. Thus, a huge crowd gathered around the elephant, and it was an occasion for great fun, especially for the children. Five blind men also lived in that town, and consequently, they also heard about the elephant. They too were eager to find out about the elephant.

Someone suggested that if they could go and feel the elephant with their hands, they could get some idea of what an elephant was like. The five blind men went to the center of the town where all the people made room for them to touch the elephant.

Later on, they sat down to discuss their experiences. One blind man, who had touched the trunk of the elephant, said that the elephant must be like a thick tree branch. Another who touched the tail said the elephant probably looked like a snake or rope. The third man, who touched the leg, said the shape of the elephant must be like a pillar. The fourth man, who touched the ear, said that the elephant must be like a huge fan; while the fifth, who touched the side, said it must be like a wall.

They sat for hours and argued, each being sure that his view was correct. Obviously, they were all correct from their own point of view, but no one was quite willing to listen to the others. Finally, they decided to go to the wise man of the village and ask him who was correct. The wise man said, "Each one of you is correct; and each one of you is wrong. Because each one of you had only touched one part of the elephant's body. Thus you only have a partial view of the animal. If you put your partial views together, you will get an idea of what an elephant looks like."

The moral of the fable is that each one of us sees things exclusively within our own point of view.

Old Views of Addiction

Chemical addiction is much like the elephant in this old fable. Everyone knows it exists but until recently only some of its parts had been described by experts from different fields.

In the 1800's religious leaders decided that alcohol itself was the root of the problem and "demon rum" was labeled as the substance that should be expelled from the lives of Americans. The Temperance Movement of 1928 grew out of the idea that giving up drinking would lead to moral living, especially for those who drank too much and became "morally depraved."

That alcoholism and later addiction to other drugs might be a disease was first advanced by a signer of the Declaration of Independence, Dr. Benjamin Rush. Rush argued that "habitual drunkenness should be regarded not as a bad habit but as a disease" characterized by "a palsy of the will." It was not until 1966 that the American Medical Association (AMA) declared alcoholism to be a disease (in 1956 the AMA declared it an "illness"). According to the AMA, the disease is characterized by "preoccupation with alcohol and loss of control over its consumption" leading to "physical disability and impaired emotional, occupational, and/or social adjustments" as direct consequences.

While the AMA declared alcoholism to be an illness in 1956, the drafters of the policy made no attempt to define the cause of the disease, but like others who attempted definitions, they described the major symptom of alcoholism, the uncontrollable desire to drink regardless of the negative consequences that drinking brings about. For some years after this declaration the primary group of doctors who chose to treat alcoholics and addicts were psychiatrists. Most psychiatrists believed that the uncontrollable obsession was really a symptom of a deeper problem or problems. Alcoholics were thus seen as clinically depressed or anxious people who needed a mix of talk therapy (e.g., getting to the childhood root of the depression or anxiety or low self-esteem) and medication. For years alcoholics were given benzodiazepines which themselves are addicting and can react lethally when taken with alcohol. Not until recently was there research that proved that alcohol taken in large doses over time causes depression in alcoholics rather than the position taken by the psychiatrists of 1970.

Behavioral psychologists in the 1970's and 80's looked

at the alcoholic and decided that the excessive drinking was simply "maladaptive behavior" and could be changed by behavior therapy. In the 1980's there arose a school of "Moderation Management" whose aim through interventions like biofeedback was to help the alcoholic find the number of drinks that was both safe and satisfying to the drinker . The founder of the movement eventually left the group and joined Alcoholics Anonymous (AA).

All of the groups who attempted to define alcoholism prior to 1970 resembled the characters in the "Elephant and Blind Men" fable. The Temperance Movement looked at the alcoholic and found his moral lapses to be the fault of the substance. The AMA defined the disease by its chief symptom, the inability of the alcoholic to control his drinking. The psychiatrist whose work is healing the psyche found the primary symptom to be but a reflection of a psychological problem, while the behaviorists saw only the alcoholic's behavior as needing correction. While addiction to alcohol was then as it is now a disease that takes an enormous toll on individuals, families, and society, no effort had been made to study the disease from the perspective of all that was known about alcohol and human biology. The elephant remained a collection of parts, some seen clearly, some not.

The Breakthrough

In 1970 Dr. James Milam, a clinical psychologist, published the Emergent Comprehensive Concept of Alcoholism. Prior to writing this paper now out of print, he had surveyed not only all the existing literature on alcoholism but also all research on alcohol and its effects. He had looked at existing treatment for the disease as well as reading literature about Alcoholics Anonymous (AA) and talking to long time members of AA

Dr. Milam concluded that alcoholism was not, as many members of the medical community believed, a psychological illness. All the evidence pointed clearly to the nature of alcoholism as physiological. Alcoholism, he declared, is a biogenic illness whose roots lie in a genetic predisposition and a consequent malfunctioning of various organs of the body, from the liver to the central nervous system. His findings in part were based on two studies conducted by Dr. Donald Goodwin as the basis for genetic influences in the victim of alcoholism. Goodwin studied children who were taken from alcoholic parents at birth and raised by non-alcoholic relatives. Goodwin found that these children had a high rate of addiction even though they were free of the environmental influences of the birth parents. Conversely children taken from non-alcoholic parents and raised by alcoholic parents had a much lower rate of developing alcoholism despite being raised in an alcoholic home. It was evidence that nature not nurture was the reason people became alcoholic.

In the Emergent Comprehensive Concept, Dr. Milam gives a deep bow to the founding of Alcoholics Anonymous (AA) in 1935 and the resultant understanding of the process of the disease. The idea that an alcoholic will forever be susceptible to alcohol and must never drink again came from the experiences of AA members. From the stories of AA members it also became clear that how much a person drinks is not relevant to diagnosing the disease. It is the progressive consequences of drinking too much that define alcoholism, those consequences being physical, behavioral, spiritual, emotional, and social. The experiences of AA members laid the groundwork for decades of further study by researchers on how the body and brain of the alcoholic were different from those of the non-alcoholic drinker.

In 1981 Dr. Milam published "Under the Influence" with Katherine Ketcham and expanded upon the information in the Emergent Comprehensive Concept of Alcoholism. In the book Dr. Milam explains the effects of alcohol on the body and the stages of alcoholism. He discusses physical and psychological craving and the chief symptom of addiction, loss of control. Dr. Milam then outlines a treatment regimen aimed at addressing all the components of the disease and the necessary steps the recovering addict must take to lead a successful life. That philosophy and practice has informed the programs at Lakeside since 1983.

What Science Tells Us about Alcoholism Today

Almost 40 years have passed since Dr. Milam published his first book outlining the evidence that addiction to alcohol and other drugs is a biogenic disease. Since then, and especially in the last 20 years, a focused effort to study the nature of addiction has resulted in a better and deeper understanding of the nature of the disease, the process by which people become addicted, and an affirmation of treatment protocols described in "Under the Influence."

The theory that addiction was a secondary ailment reflecting psychic wounds from the past was exploded when neuroscience began looking at the one organ that could cause all the chief symptoms of addiction. With the advantage of animal studies and modern imaging techniques, researchers found that the seat of addiction lay in the human brain. The organ that dictates all human emotions, thoughts, and behavior, malfunctions in the alcoholic/addict so that all psychoactive drugs set off the loss of control which leads to the obsessive craving and singular focus of the victim on ingesting more of a drug to the exclusion of all other demands of everyday life.

In the summer of 2011, the American Medical

Association published the first definition of addiction since the initial pronouncement in 1966. Addiction is, the definition states, "a chronic brain disorder" and a "primary disease," meaning that it is not the result of other causes such as emotional or psychological issues. "The disease creates distortions in thinking, feeling and perceptions which drives people to behave in ways that are not understandable to those around them. Simply put, addiction is not a choice."

The Disease of Addiction – Science versus Learned Attitudes

There is now scientific certainty that addiction to alcohol and other drugs is a disease much like other medical diseases suffered by human beings. An accepted definition of a medical disease (Lewis, D.C., 1997) is that:

1. it has a clear biological basis and
2. a set of unique, identifiable signs and symptoms and
3. a predictable course and outcome and
4. an inability to control the course of the disease.

With the discovery of the genetically predisposed neurotransmission system in the brain of the addict, the biological basis of addiction has been confirmed. The signs and symptoms of the disease – tolerance, withdrawal, more use of the drug than is intended, the inability to control use, increased time and effort to obtain the drug, neglect of important human activities and continued use despite knowledge of clear problems – can be assessed and rated. The predictable stages of addiction are well known and the sad outcome of the disease, if untreated, is deterioration of the victim's body, mind, and spirit. In its nature addiction has been compared by medical researchers to other chronic diseases like coronary heart disease, diabetes, and hypertension. All these diseases can be arrested if the victims follow a life-long treatment regimen and accept the limitations that the disease imposes. As an example, in the case of Type II diabetes, the recovering patient must follow a strict diet, usually lose weight and adopt an exercise regimen. Finally, while science has discovered the method in which the neurotransmission system in the addict's brain malfunctions, there is no research that provides any hope that the system can be desensitized to psychoactive drugs. It is impossible to exclude addiction from the list of medical diseases without also excluding diseases like diabetes and heart disease.

Despite the Science...

A review of the public opinion polls that George

Gallup took for decades about the nature of alcoholism shows that the overwhelming majority of Americans believe addiction to be a medical disease. In the last polls taken in the 1990's over 90% of respondents agreed that alcoholism is a disease and should be treated as such. But in a poll conducted in 2006 the Gallup researchers asked immediate family members of addicts to rate seven items as to whether each was a major factor, a minor factor, or not a factor in their loved one's addiction. Three items received the highest scores as major factors in their view of addiction – "lacking willpower (54%)," "living in a situation where drugs or alcohol were easy to obtain (54%), and "a psychological illness such as depression or anxiety (50%)." Only 34% of the family members listed "a genetic trait they were born with" as a major factor. At first glance it appears very strange that the people whom one would think would know the most about the nature of addiction respond most naïvely to questions about the disease.

It is doubtful that family members of diabetics would rank "lacking willpower" or "living in a situation where sugar-rich foods are available" as major factors in their loved ones' disease. So it is reasonable to ask why there is such a disconnect between the beliefs of many families of addicts and the proven science which has become widely promoted.

We Believe What We See

The answer lies in the ways human beings learn. From a young age we learn from teachers and books, but we also learn from our personal experience. Our experience can shape our beliefs and attitudes and indeed can countermand what books tell us. The patient who learns he is diabetic may, like an addict, go through a period of denial because the thought of having the disease is unpleasant and the program of changing his lifestyle to recover is even more unpleasant. He may, as studies have shown, not follow his physician's orders and become even sicker. (Less than 50% of diabetics do in fact stay on the prescribed regimen, and many suffer numerous relapses.) But the family of the diabetic will not experience the hurtful, irresponsible behaviors and total personality change that the family of an addict may witness in the mid to late stages of addiction. The addict's behavior appears to be purposely willful.

Objectively, the reasons for differences in the families' experiences are easy to explain. The biological origin of diabetes is a malfunctioning pancreas that causes all the consequent physical maladies for the victim. There is no direct or indirect effect on the victim's power of reasoning or his ability to control his emotions. The addict on the other hand has the misfortune to have a malfunctioning brain, specifically the mesolimbic reward system, which overrides the part of the brain, the frontal cortex, which enables him to reason, make moral, responsible decisions, and react responsibly to those he loves. The addict's body, mind, and spirit become focused on one goal—satisfying and protecting his/her addiction.

For most addicts the changes in thought, feeling, and behavior happen over time in a slow insidious manner. By the time the family takes note of the addict's denial, defensive emotional outbursts and irresponsible behavior the victim's brain has already been hijacked. The loss of control is often seen by the unknowing family as a willful disregard of family values and responsibility rather than as a consequence of an altered brain. Pleas of "Please stop this" go seemingly unheard and the family becomes frustrated, saddened, and angered, all very human reactions to difficult people.

Take a Step Back

One of the central reasons for the creation of this guide is to provide families with a chance to step out of the emotional turmoil of living with an addict and learn addiction from a different point of view. The first principle of the science of addiction is that like any disease, the victim has no control over contracting it. Once contracted, the disease overrides the alcoholic/addict's willpower and impairs the ability to make intelligent, responsible decisions.

The nature of addiction does not excuse the addict from responsibility for the consequences of the disease. Once the victim enters treatment, understands the disease, and receives the tools necessary to arrest the disease, the addict is responsible like the diabetic or coronary patient for following a regimen of recovery. Relapse, if it occurs, can be traced most simply, as with diabetes and coronary heart disease, to the patient's not following the prescription for recovery.

<u>Addiction and the Altered Brain</u>

The human brain has often been compared to a very complex computer. A computer takes in data and processes it through a set of basic units called semiconductors. The data is relayed from unit to unit by electric current. The amount of current and its route through the semiconductors determine what the computer produces. The basic units of the brain are billions of neurons. Our experience is processed by sending electrical impulses and certain chemicals, neurotransmitters, from neuron to neuron. How big an impulse and how much of a certain neurotransmitter is discharged determine what we think, feel, and do. There are many different kinds of neurotransmitters and each sends a different message to a neuron depending on what kind of experience is being processed. Some of the more active neurotransmitters are dopamine , serotonin and the endorphins.

Where Addiction is Located

One of the most primitive parts of the human brain is the limbic system. The limbic system or, more specifically, the mesolimbic reward system, regulates our ability to feel pleasure. When we feel pleasure in an activity like eating or sex we seek to repeat that activity just as early man did to ensure his survival. The limbic system is also responsible for our experiencing other positive and negative emotions.

In normal brain function there are circuits between the primal reward system of the brain and the frontal cortex. The frontal cortex determines our ability to reason and make judgments on whether or not a given action is wise. We may for instance look at a piece of rich chocolate cake and feel a pleasant urge to eat it but then reason that the short-term pleasure would result in unwanted calories and a bigger waistline.

The pleasure generating neurotransmitter that is released in the limbic reward system is dopamine. Like all neurotransmitters dopamine moves from one neuron to the next and attaches to a receptor site. Once it is attached to a receptor site a transporter on the sending cell recycles the dopamine for future use. This process is repeated millions of times a day in different parts of the brain with different neurotransmitters depending on the experience we encounter. We learn as human beings because circuits are established over our lifetimes that ensure that communication between different parts of the brain is effective and efficient.

Psychoactive drugs are chemicals. They infiltrate the brain's communication system and interrupt the way cells normally send, receive, and process information. Some drugs mimic neurotransmitters, but they act differently on receptors and lead to abnormal messages being transmitted. Other drugs cause neurons to release abnormally high amounts of neurotransmitters or prevent the recycling of these brain chemicals. It is the flooding of the reward circuit with dopamine that causes the euphoria or sedation that the drug taker seeks. For most people who drink or take a drug the feeling passes fairly quickly as the drug is metabolized in their bodies.

The Addicted Brain is Different

The scientific position today is that the addict's

neurotransmission system is genetically predisposed to be different from that of a non-addict. There is a genetic vulnerability that leads to a "dysregulation" of the mesolimbic dopamine system with the ingestion of drugs. The dysregulation causes the alcoholic/addict to take more of the drug (increased tolerance) in order to get the same initial effect. At some point, instantly in some cases, and years in others, the dysregulation alters the neurotransmission system so that the brain will always be over-sensitized to psychoactive drugs. At this point there is no voluntary choice to drink or take drugs: the brain devotes itself to seeking and finding the substances that make the addict feel "normal". The structure of the neural system has mutated and with it the victim of addiction passes over into a different state of being. It is therefore not the physical properties of addictive drugs that determine who becomes addicted. It is the genetic predisposition rooted in the altered limbic reward system that causes the addict to reprioritize all other meaningful life activities in favor of finding and taking drugs and/or alcohol.

Scientists began to prove Dr. Milam's assertion of

genetic vulnerability when they genetically altered mice so that the subjects preferred alcohol (and later cocaine) to all other substances, drinking to the point of death. The neurological changes in addicts' brains were confirmed with the use of brain PET scans which showed clear areas of decreased brain function in actively using addicts. The changes afflicted not only the limbic system but also the frontal cortex, the seat of reason and logic. Addiction then not only produces the uncontrollable urge to drink/use despite disastrous consequences. It also impairs the victim's ability to reason and to consider the needs of his family, friends, and employers/teachers.

Powerful Triggers

What makes the craving so powerful is the psychological process rooted in the reward system. Every time the victim of addiction takes a drug or drinks alcohol the event is recorded in the preconscious primal brain. All the people, places, moods, and events that the addict associates with the act of drug taking became triggers or cues setting up the same urge every time they are encountered. Environment therefore can play a role in triggering the addiction already inherent in the genetically predisposed neurotransmission system in the brain. This phenomenon also explains in part the process of relapse. If a recovering addict is not actively working a program of recovery and encounters a stressor which he always relieved in the past by drinking he has little defense against the power of the urge to drink again. One of the functions of treatment is to give the patient the tools to recognize triggers and deal with them quickly.

The brain, unlike the computer, has an amazing ability to correct the effects of dysregulation that addiction causes so long as no more psychoactive drugs are ingested. In treatment the patient is warned about the reality of cross-tolerance to drugs and the importance of avoiding all drugs of dependence.

Alcohol

Alcohol is the legal drug of choice for most Americans and it remains, after 25 years, the drug most often cited by our patients. There are myths that still abound about alcohol and its effects (e.g., "you don't get drunk on beer") but the reality is that alcohol taken in excess over time can have long term effects on the human body and brain.

Alcohol's effect is initially a stimulant, as can be witnessed at any cocktail party when the noise level grows and conversation becomes animated. Part of the stimulant effect is due to the empty calories that alcohol provides. Alcohol is, however a depressive or sedative drug, and overdoses caused by chugging a bottle of whisky or vodka are fatal because the nervous system shuts down usually beyond a .5% blood alcohol level. As opposed to many other drugs, alcohol is absorbed directly and unchanged into the blood stream, beginning in the mouth and continuing into the small intestine. While many different factors may affect the rate of absorption in individuals (i.e., strength, beverage, amount of food in the stomach, other chemicals in a drink) the rate of metabolism of alcohol is fixed at about one half ounce per hour. Nothing speeds that rate so the notion of coffee sobering up an intoxicated person is false. The intoxicated person may seem more alert after ingesting coffee, but the reaction time is still slowed by the alcohol.

According to 2009 estimates, over 16 million Americans are alcoholics. As a disease of the brain, like any other chemical addiction, alcoholism is not confined to any social or economic class of people. A combination of genetic and environmental influences determines who becomes alcoholic. In alcoholics, two major neurotransmission systems, the GABA system (gamma-aminobutyric acid) and the NMDA (N-methyl-D-aspartate) system are disrupted. There is also research that alcoholics find increased euphoria due to heightened endorphins and serotonin levels not found in non-alcoholics. As with all chemical addictions, alcoholism permanently affects these systems so that the brain will always malfunction when alcohol is ingested. When other drugs (e.g., benzodiazepines, other sedatives, and opiates) are added the effect of alcohol is multiplied often leading to devastating and fatal results.

Alcoholism also brings with it a host of physical problems. While the most commonly mentioned malady is cirrhosis of the liver, there are equally serious illnesses like heart disease, cancer of the stomach and esophagus, and illnesses of the immune system that alcoholism potentiates. Fetal alcohol syndrome affects alcoholic women who drink to excess during pregnancy and can cause significant developmental problems in children.

Marijuana

For many years marijuana was viewed as a "safe" recreational drug. Harvested from the leaves, flowers and stems of the hemp plant, marijuana produces a mild-euphoria, a distortion of time and sharpening of some senses. There are over 400 chemicals in marijuana, the chief among them THC which produces the sought after high. Physiologically, the drug acts partly like a barbiturate and partly like a hallucinogen. Marijuana suppresses rapid eye movement (REM) non-dream sleep and many users describe restless sleep habits.

Like other addictive drugs, marijuana stimulates the limbic system in the brain and therefore the craving mechanism. The drug leeches onto fatty areas of the body and an addict will test positive for THC for as long as 2 months after last use. Because marijuana distorts the perception of time it also slows reaction time and therefore poses a hazard in driving a car or operating a machine.

Psychologically, marijuana can induce panic attacks especially in first time users. Paranoia is also common taking the form of fear of being discovered by police or family. People addicted to marijuana suffer what is called an "amotivational syndrome" marked by apathy, poor concentration, withdrawal from friends and family and a loss of interest in any kind of achievement. Science is not sure whether marijuana induces this attitude or whether it may be due to damage to cerebral functions. Teenagers who become addicted to marijuana lose all interest in school and seem incapable of normal learning. It is therefore essential that early interventions be taken to prevent a lifetime learning deficit in teens whose drug of necessity is marijuana.

Withdrawal from marijuana is marked by irritability, general discomfort and loss of appetite. Withdrawal from this drug is not as severe as with opiate drugs but the symptoms may last longer.

The So Called Club Drugs

There are a number of drugs that came about in the club scene that began in the 1980's and have been marketed illegally since then.

MDMA (Ecstasy)

Ecstasy is a drug that was legal until 1985 when it was made a Schedule I drug. Its appeal is that it causes a feeling of well being and connectedness in its user. Once recommended by mental health therapists, in current form it is often mixed with other contaminants that are dangerous in themselves. The drug is neurotoxic in that prolonged use can damage the process of creating serotonin in the brain. Increased doses over time produce a diminished high and an increase in undesirable consequences like restlessness and teeth gnashing. In some addicts severe effects have been found like drastic change in blood pressure, tachycardia and renal failure. Problems can remain long after last use, including depression, anxiety, increased compulsiveness and sleep disturbance.

Ketamine

Ketamine was created as an anesthetic for animals. It is classified as a "dissociative anesthetic" and when taken by humans cause a sense of detachment, fragmentation and disconnection from the general environment. A dose of Ketamine lasts about one hour. Higher doses have a more intense effect and users have been described as zombie like since they appear to have no awareness of their surroundings. Like other drugs described here it does release dopamine which in turn can cause the craving of addiction.

Opioids

Opioids are a class of drugs used to alleviate pain. There are natural opiates that are derived from the opium poppy such as morphine and codeine and there are also semi-synthetic compounds like heroin. Methadone is also an opioid.

Opioids have been used for centuries to relieve pain, especially the acute pain of injuries or post operative trauma. Addiction to opioids has also existed for centuries. The effect of opiates on the user is to produce a dreamy euphoric state. Unlike some other drugs, opiates by and large have a short half-life so ingestion must be repeated frequently to forestall withdrawal. At the same time tolerance to opiates is created quickly, so that the addict requires increased doses over a short time span.

Heroin of course is an illegal drug and the quality of the drug sold will vary greatly from dealer to dealer. Some heroin will be very pure while other batches will be mixed with various contaminants such as talc and starch. The danger of overdose and death is high when an addict does not know the strength of the drug injected or snorted or smoked. There are also tremendous health risks in the sharing of needles. Heroin addicts getting into recovery are dismayed to find that they also have to battle HIV or hepatitis contracted by using dirty needles.

A Dangerous Synthetic

Special mention must be made of synthetic opiates intended as legal prescriptions. Among younger patients (18-27 years old) addiction to Oxycontin has spread rapidly. Oxycontin (trade name for Oxycodone) is a popular pain management drug used because it is released over an extended period of time and prevents the peaks and valleys of pain in patients taking it. It has become widely used by adolescents and young adults who crush the pills and snort or inject them thus having immediate access to the whole narcotic load of the pill. Taken from parents' prescriptions or bought on the street, Oxycontin, like other opiates, produces significant craving for more, coupled with an increasing tolerance to the drug. Withdrawal from Oxycontin, or any other synthetic opiate (e.g. Vicodin, Percodan, Dilaudid) is uncomfortable. It is our experience at Lakeside that young opiate addicts have a difficult time in treatment for the first week and a higher percentage of these patients leave treatment against medical advice than patients addicted to non opiate drugs and / or alcohol.

In the last few years a sad trend has occurred among young people addicted to oxycontin. As illegal consumption rose the cost of oxycontin on the street also spiked higher. Addicts have been lured back to heroin as a cheaper, but just as potentially lethal substitute.

Methadone has been used for years as a "maintenance" drug for opiate addicts. Methadone itself however is a synthetic opiate that can be abused and is often sold on the street. Another drug Buprenorphine has been used in withdrawal from opiates supposedly because it is safe and cannot be used to generate a "high." Recently however there are reports of this drug being crushed and snorted thereby giving the sought after euphoria.

We at Lakeside believe that we always need to seek

better ways to ease opiate withdrawal for our patients. We do not and will not however dispense any drug that has the power to continue the dysfunction of the neurotransmitter system so that the patient cannot experience what a drug free life in recovery is like.

Stimulant Drugs

Drugs like cocaine and amphetamine increase activity in a number of parts of the brain. The effect on the user is seen as energetic euphoria, heightened motor activity, often non-stop talkativeness, and an inability to sleep. In mid to late stages the addict has almost no appetite and engages in strange repetitive behaviors.

Cocaine is a short acting drug that is either snorted, injected or smoked. Because it is an illegal drug, the addict will usually hide his consumption but as with any addiction he will deny his use. Teenagers will invent any manner of excuses to deny that cocaine their parents find is their's (e.g. "a friend asked me to hold it for him; I didn't know what it was"). After prolonged use the addict will "crash," sleeping for long periods and falling into days of depression as well as an inability to experience pleasure. Psychological craving for cocaine is strong and may last many months.

The amphetamine class of drugs includes Dexadrine, methamphetamine, Ritalin, and mixtures like Adderall.

Amphetamines have a longer duration of effect than cocaine. Some are used in the treatment of medical conditions like narcolepsy (sleeping sickness), ADHD and weight control.

Methamphetamine is the most abused drug in this class, most likely because it can be produced easily, is highly euphoric and can be sold at huge profits. It can also fairly easily lead to an overdose and appears to have long lasting effects on brain function when taken over a protracted period of time. Like cocaine it produces increased motor activity and repetitive behaviors. Most addicts complain that they don't feel "normal" when they stop taking the drug although this lack of imbalance does pass in recovery. Meth has the same route of administration as cocaine – snorting, injection, or smoking. Like cocaine, methamphetamine creates a prolonged period of craving in the addict. Tolerance to both cocaine and amphetamines develops rapidly so that larger doses are needed to produce the desired effect.

Stimulant drugs are most dangerous to the cardiac

system of the addict. They increase blood pressure and heart rate. While they increase the workload of the heart they also constrict the arteries leading to the heart. The result can be anything from arrhythmias (rapid heartbeat) to heart attacks. Addicts can also suffer dehydration, nutritional deficiencies and endocrine abnormalities. Meth addicts often come to have "meth mouth," a combination of badly decayed teeth and shrinking gums scarred by decreased blood supply.

While there are no major physiological symptoms of withdrawal for cocaine and methamphetamine, there are often severe psychological after effects. Detoxing patients feel anxious and fidget constantly. They show little ability to feel pleasure for anything around them and a persistent lack of energy. Relapse is relatively certain without intensive treatment and commitment to a highly structured recovery plan.

The Stages of Addiction

The disease of addiction like other diseases presents in serial stages as it progresses to take hold of its victim. While it is true that with some people, especially adolescents, there appears to be an "instant onset" of addiction in most addicts the disease takes 2-5 years to manifest itself fully. This slow onset is of course one of the reasons that many addicts are not identified until the mid stages of their illness.

What follows is a description of the "typical" progression of addiction in an alcoholic. While the victim addicted to other drugs may switch drugs (e.g. many from marijuana to cocaine or methamphetamine or opiates) the stages of addiction are marked by similar mental, emotional, behavioral and spiritual changes. There is also little difference in the type of treatment required to arrest the disease.

The Case of John M.

At 36 years old, John M. was just about where he

wanted to be in life. He had a good wife, Maureen, who loved him and his kids, a boy, 16 years old, a girl, 12, and another girl, 8. After working for ten years at an insurance company he had recently been promoted to a manager's position supervising six claim agents.

John and Maureen had close friends, couples who often visited each other for drinks and card games. John was known as a cheerful guy who liked beer and held it very well. There was always enough beer and liquor in the house for visitors and the get-togethers at John and Maureen's house often lasted well after midnight with everyone pleasantly high and laughing. John knew he was wittier and sharper after a few drinks.

In his new job John felt he was expected to take his staff out for drinks frequently after work. He made sure everyone had enough drinks to relax and usually would be the last to leave the bar. Increasingly he came home later and later, missing dinner and even the kids' bedtime. After the first few times Maureen became upset and dressed him down. John was defensive, proclaiming that one or more of his employees had problems and it was his duty to help them work things out.

Eight months after beginning his new job, John was driving home, once again staying over four hours at the bar. A police car appeared behind him and motioned him over to the curb. Smelling alcohol on John, the police officer administered the field sobriety test. John appeared to complete the physical test easily, but he blew a 0.20 in the blood alcohol test and was charged with a driving under the influence. John arrived home very remorseful and ashamed. He told Maureen that it would never happen again and with the aid of a good DUI lawyer got the charge reduced to negligent driving. The $5,000 fee, however, put a big dent in the family budget. John gave up drinking for two weeks and came home promptly after work each night. At the end of two weeks John started drinking again, at first scrupulously consuming only two beers a night. In a month he was claiming to have had only his two beer maximum but also sneaking drinks from the bottle of vodka he kept in the car.

The First Symptoms

The first sign of a potential problem for John is that he has a higher tolerance for alcohol than others. He can drink beer and not feel "high" until the fourth or fifth can. To those around him this is an admirable trait. "John can hold his beer very well." The increased ability to drink is actually an early symptom of alcoholism. John's neurotransmission system is probably suffering a deficit in those neurotransmitters or receptors that alcohol affects. After a few drinks he begins to feel not only "normal" but better than normal. He can speak more clearly and be more sociable than he can without alcohol in his body. He remembers and treasures the nights when everyone found him to be the funniest, sharpest person at the party. In the same manner addicts who are introduced to drugs other than alcohol normally remember later in their addiction how good they felt when they first started using the drug. The fruitless search of addiction is a return to the feeling state of the first experience with drugs. One of the later symptoms of addiction is what is referred to as "Euphoric Recall", a memory of only the good experiences of drug consumption regardless of the disastrous consequence that have occurred in later years.

John is also in the early phase of denial, a psychological trait that marks all addiction. He believes totally in his motivation for taking his employees to a bar to wind down and discuss work problems. He becomes righteously defensive about these lengthening sessions and never once thinks that he could hold the same kind of sessions in a coffee shop.

Denial is a common human defense mechanism used to protect the psyche from truths we do not wish to face, like death or disease. There are many forms of denial, from rationalization to minimization, and the addict becomes adept at all of them as the disease progresses. Denial acts like an impervious shield around the disease unless and until the damage to the life of the addict is impossible for him to ignore.

Denial is not lying. When an addict declares "I'm not as bad as that guy" he declares what is a fact to him. When an addict declares that he drinks because of the stress of his job he is telling the truth as he can perceive it – even if the stress is caused by poor performance due to absences and hangovers. Those around him are easily taken in for a good period of time because the denials seem true. It is often not until the ravages of the disease are apparent that those who care for the addict find his reasons completely without merit.

John at this point in his drinking is also exhibiting another symptom of the disease – continuing to drink despite adverse consequences. The non-addict drinker would after receiving an expensive, emotionally painful legal charge like a DUI, stop drinking altogether or limit himself without any effort to one or two drinks. John stops drinking for a brief period in part to show himself and his loved ones that he can. He then decides that he will develop moderation in his use of alcohol. He finds quickly that this route is impossible since once he has one or two beers the deeply rooted craving circuit in his brain demands more. John does not analyze his concealment of the amount he drinks. He knows only the amount of alcohol needed for him to feel "normal" and erase the nameless anxiety and tension that he feels when he has not drank enough.

The Middle Stage

John's preoccupation with alcohol grows but he justifies it to himself with the rationalization that it is stress related. He now drinks at lunch and usually by himself since none of his coworkers drink until after work. Maureen is suspicious that his claims of limiting his drinking are false. John ceases his after work sessions at the bar with his employees, preferring to go alone where no one will question how much alcohol he puts away.

John begins experiencing terrible hangovers, some of which leave him almost immobile. He has a variety of explanations for his family to explain how bad he feels, a virus, a stomach flu, insomnia. On most days he uses super human willpower to get himself to work where his excuses continue. On some days he calls in sick.

As getting and drinking enough alcohol becomes the center of his life other responsibilities go unattended. He misses school functions for the kids and is often late with reports for his boss at work. He becomes distant with his employees and develops resentments against them believing that somehow his problems are all their fault. He snaps at people at work for the slightest errors and rails against his kids if they bring home less than perfect report cards. The next day he feels shame and regret but cannot bring himself to apologize. Sometimes he buys expensive gifts which he can't afford to atone for his harshness.

At this point John knows that his drinking is not normal. He tries all manner of techniques to try and control it. He attempts to ration himself after work and at home and switches the kinds of alcohol he drinks. None of the methods are successful and his moods grow darker. His overt defense is that he is a victim of an uncaring employer and a nagging wife. He goes to bars alone and converses with anyone who shares his bleak worldview and like him takes comfort in drinking. He does not take note of the fact that the people he talks with are not the kind of people he would have as friends a few years ago.

John's boss calls him in to confront him about his declining work performance. John is initially defensive but his boss is persuasive in showing him the evidence of his sub par behavior. John becomes contrite and vows to turn things around. John is fearful of losing his job and vows to himself to stop drinking. His willpower lasts 2 days and he begins again to try to control his drinking during the work week. He has trouble concentrating on simple tasks and is often frozen in his ability to make decisions. He begins to drink in the morning in order to think straight.

The Symptoms Multiply

In the middle stage of the disease the victim begins to suffer another symptom of addiction, the pangs of withdrawal. Everyone who has ever had a hangover has suffered mild withdrawal from alcohol. The dry mouth, headache, queasy stomach and edginess are signs that the body is reacting to the absence of the substance.

There are 2 kinds of withdrawal. Some drugs like alcohol and opioids can inflict severe physical withdrawal symptoms when they leave the body. Victims can experience some or all of these discomforts: sweating, muscle aches and spasms, heart palpitation, tremors or shaking, difficulty breathing, nausea, vomiting or diarrhea. It is important that the addict in withdrawal from these drugs receives medical supervision since some cases of withdrawal can be life threatening.

Other drugs (cocaine, methamphetamine, marijuana, club drugs) have little apparent physical withdrawal symptoms but strong psychological symptoms. The craving to use the drug again is often overwhelming in the first few weeks and can cause anxiety, restlessness, severe irritability, inability to concentrate, insomnia and depression. Detoxification from psychoactive drugs does not constitute a treatment regimen but only the first stage in allowing the addict to participate in a program that addresses the psychosocialemotional changes that must be made for recovery.

In the middle stage of the disease the addict knows that something is very wrong with his drinking and/or using drugs. He tries every imaginable method to control use but meets with failure. For most addicts this is the period in which rationalization takes over. "Yes, I drink/use too much but look at the problems I have to deal with." As the ability to reason logically is overridden by the primal brain the addict can not look at his life and understand that the problems he encounters have been caused by his drinking/using. His growing isolation, estrangement from friends and family, and poor performance at work or school grow directly from his uncontrollable use of psychoactive drugs.

The middle stage alcoholic/addict is in constant emotional turmoil. He may become a perfectionist with others in order to hide his own failings. He resents anyone who seems to be successful and begins to see success of any kind as futile. Whatever his emotion it is augmented by the disruption in his limbic system and anger becomes rage very quickly while regret may turn into an hour of sulking. Depending on the drug of necessity (falsely labeled the drug of choice by some) the addict may experience tremors and other signs of withdrawal if he goes a few hours without the drug in his body. Alcoholics will spend hours on the telephone late at night justifying their behavior to the increasingly shrinking number of friends who try to be sympathetic. He will borrow money wherever he can but since his spiritual value system is collapsing he may also take money that is not his and rationalize his theft.

Addiction is a chronic disease and if it is not interrupted in the early or middle stage, the life of the late stage addict is predictable and sad. The singular focus in taking the drug separates the addict from friends, family and livelihood. The addict suffers a wide range of physical ailments from heart and liver disease to respiratory ailments and various cancers. With many drugs also comes brain damage in the form of severe cognitive impairment, confabulation (creating stories to account for his failing memory) and hallucinations. The late stage addict, however, is far from hopeless and at Lakeside we have witnessed countless late stage addicts be reborn through the inpatient treatment process. Unlike other chronic diseases whose severe physical consequences dictate whether a patient is terminal, chemical addiction can be successfully treated as long as the addict is open to new learning and believes that change is possible.

The case history described in this guide happens to relate the story of an alcoholic. If we changed the name of the drug the same pattern of addiction will emerge. All drugs that affect the release of dopamine in the mesolimbic reward system will have the same effect on the addict's brain and will lead to the same pain and the same syndrome of disease symptoms. One of our lectures in treatment is called "A Drug is a Drug is a Drug" and its goal is to make our patients aware that they have to avoid psychoactive drugs completely in recovery.

Increasingly patients arrive at treatment having used a wide variety of drugs. While adult patients may admit to using only alcohol, younger patients, especially in the 15-25 age bracket, will confess to taking whatever drug was available even if they preferred one drug over another.

Adolescent Addiction

There is no difference between the nature and process of addiction in an adolescent or an adult. There is, however, a significant difference in the speed of the stages of addiction in an adolescent compared to that of an adult. To know the reason for that difference we must understand the difference between the adolescent brain and the adult brain.

Remember that the seat of addiction lies in the limbic reward system, the part of the brain that regulates emotions and motivations, especially those that relate to survival such as fear, anger and pleasure. It not only urged early humans to take pleasure in activities like eating and sex; it also allowed them to fight or flee when faced with threats to their existence. All of these reactions are very primal. Another part of the brain, the frontal lobes, allowed humans to make rational decisions, solve problems, develop a personality and understand the consequences of their actions.

Learning is produced by the creation of neural

synapses in response to processing experiences and reasoning out the correct action(s). The adult who first drinks or uses drugs in his/her late twenties will initially control overuse due to the expected unwanted physical or social consequences (i.e. hangovers or embarrassment). It usually takes two to five years for addiction to be triggered as the limbic system switches on the craving, which is the benchmark of addiction.

Science has verified that the critical frontal lobes of the brain do not develop fully until a person is 20 to 25 years old. The adolescent then is forced to process all experiences through the limbic system and consequently has little ability to assess the risk/benefit of any experience. A parent may warn their child about the dangers of speeding in a car, but the teenager feels only the thrill of driving fast and the sense of power it provides. The "go" part of the brain, the limbic reward system, has at best a faulty "stop" mechanism, the underdeveloped frontal lobes.

Given this reality, it is easy to see why so many teenage tragedies involve alcohol and other drugs. With little ability to measure the consequences of drinking and using drugs, adolescents feel only the euphoric high that drugs provide and place themselves in danger of lethal driving accidents, overdoses and other high risk behaviors. The desire to repeat the behavior is powerful especially if no negative consequences are suffered. Most adolescents spend some part of their teenage years experimenting with alcohol/drugs and begin making more rational decisions about use as their brain's frontal lobe develops and reason dictates that the risks of drug taking outweigh the benefits.

This natural development however does not occur for the 11-15% of adolescents genetically predisposed to addiction. The initial high they experience is much stronger than that of non-addicts, and the urge to take more of the drug is much stronger. Whatever rational resistance may be operating in an adolescent addict's mind is often swept away quickly by the intense pleasure derived from the substances. Mark's story reveals a fairly typical pattern that we see at Lakeside.

Mark, 16, came to his sophomore year of high school

with above average grades and a reputation as being a quiet but respectful student. His parents reported that he was generally a cooperative child except for some adolescent "growing pains."

In late September he went to a party where a friend offered him a toke from a marijuana joint. Mark experienced the most pleasure he had ever felt in his young life. The next week Mark found the friend's supplier and bought some pot using money he had saved from a summer job. He began smoking on weekends with a new group of friends who also provided alcohol at their gatherings. By November Mark drank or smoked every day and began cutting classes. When his parents grew concerned about his grades, he got angry and accused teachers of having it in for him. His parents gave him strict time limits on staying out which he kept for two days, then failed to appear until two in the morning. He tried again to limit his use of alcohol and drugs to the weekend but he found that he was too much on edge and couldn't concentrate on anything at home or at school. Mark became volatile, either shutting himself in his room or screaming at his parents. He was sent home from school for fighting and complained that the other boy picked on him. By the beginning of January Mark was interested only in getting high, He stole money from his mother's purse or his father's wallet to buy pot and alcohol. When his parents found him passed out near the front door one night they knew that Mark had a problem they couldn't solve and brought him to Lakeside for an assessment.

Not all adolescent addiction progresses this quickly but Mark's case is not that unusual. Some adolescent addicts can mask the symptoms of the disease from parents for long periods of time. The acting out, mood swings and decline in performance at school are often mistaken for "phases" that parents hope teenagers will grow out of. If the mood swings become persistent parents often mistake the behavior for a mental health issue and take the child to a psychologist who may not ask the right questions to uncover the real problem, the addiction to alcohol and drugs.

The prevalent drugs of addiction consumed by

adolescents admitted to Lakeside are alcohol and marijuana. While addicted teenagers may take any drug that is available these drugs are easy to obtain and relatively inexpensive.

Many teenagers will also raid family medicine cabinets for any painkilling drugs prescribed to other family members. The combination of opiates and alcohol is particularly dangerous to adolescent minds and bodies.

There has been great debate about the incidence of "co-occurring disorders" (mental health issues) among adolescent addicts. There are those who would say that almost every teenage addict suffers from another mental health illness (e.g. depression, anxiety, panic disorder, anger control problems) besides addiction. At Lakeside we want to know the history of the alleged disorder before making any assessments. If the behavior began <u>before</u> any use of alcohol or drugs then there is a chance that the issue should be treated at the same time as the addiction. If however the behavior began <u>after</u> first use of alcohol/ drugs the likelihood is that it is a <u>consequence</u> of addiction and should disappear with treatment and sobriety. All of the drugs described in this guide can in the process of withdrawal cause mental and emotional disruption that appears to be symptoms of mental illness. Only a skilled assessor can distinguish drug reactions from mental health problems and only after a period of abstinence.

Do Addicts Have to Want Treatment to Recover?

One long time myth about addiction is that an addict must hit bottom in order to get sober. In the past that likely led to loved ones standing by awaiting the addict to come to a realization that help was needed. Sadly, that stance led to tragedy for many addicts who never came to that realization because they did not understand the disease that gripped them so tightly.

Growing public education has thankfully dispelled the myth. We can say with confidence that only a tiny minority of patients arrive in treatment because they decided without any prompting that they needed to change their lives. The vast majority of patients come to treatment because outside forces – family, friends, employers and the courts have told them that their addiction is harming themselves and others. Most patients arrive in treatment through external motivation, not a firmly held internal desire to get sober.

We expect that patients at admission will at best

declare that there is a problem. For some that problem is the relationships that prodded them into treatment. For others it is a grudging admission that alcohol may be a problem but marijuana is a safe alternative for them. Still others may be angry and determined to "play the game" to prove to themselves and others that they do not belong in treatment. To all our patients we present a supportive, compassionate welcome. Rather than challenging every declaration of denial we encourage each patient to enter into each lecture and each group with an open mind. Those declarations soften by the end of the first week with self-doubt appearing in week two. The power of the group and the stream of accurate information about the disease combine to whittle away defenses and plant a seed of awareness and hope.

Much rightly has been written and aired about the process of formal intervention. The process consists of a loving confrontation of an active addict by all those people who play meaningful roles in the victim's life. Its effectiveness, like that of treatment, lies in the power of a group to confront the disease. Active addicts become adept at explaining their problems away to a single person. When, however, a group of friends and loved ones echo the same list of effects to the addict, denial begins to crumble. While the addicts may be initially resentful and angry about the intrusion and judgment being rendered, most patients in treatment through an intervention become grateful that they had loving friends and family members who cared enough to intervene in the self-destruction caused by the disease. For years Lakeside has held classes in the process of intervention and the preparations necessary to perform a successful one.

Entering Treatment

After a particularly hard night when John drank till the bars closed, Maureen was waiting in the kitchen at 5:00am as John stumbled in. Maureen was pale and trembling but resolute when she told John that she couldn't take anymore. "If you don't do something about your drinking I'm divorcing you." John was stunned and tried to convince his wife that he would quit. Maureen remained adamant that he needed to get help since none of his attempts to quit drinking had succeeded for more than a few days.

John gave in and Maureen sat next to him while he opened the Yellow Pages for treatment centers. He made an appointment for an assessment to be done at a Lakeside-Milam Outpatient Center that morning.

John hoped that if he was careful in the assessment process he could get off with a few classes about alcohol. He felt comfortable with the assessing counselor and admitted that he sometimes overdid it and yes he often drank more than he intended. The counselor reviewed every area of John's life including his DUI charge and finally declared that John needed more than outpatient treatment. John was angry but he couldn't sway the counselor and with Maureen hearing the recommendation he felt he had little choice but reluctantly to enter inpatient treatment.

John entered Lakeside's Kirkland Inpatient Center in a turmoil of emotions. He was angry at being coerced by his wife, ashamed that he was reduced to being treated with a group of people who had no willpower, and more than a little afraid of being with a bunch of strangers for a month.

The Treatment Process

While we have continued to learn much about addiction and its causes over the last 25 years, we at Lakeside have never changed in our basic approach to the patients who choose to come to us. Every staff member we hire must have an unyielding belief in the ability of every patient to enter into recovery from addiction, a pervasive empathy for the pain that each patient has suffered, and the ability to communicate warmth and hope each day at work.

All patients entering inpatient treatment at Lakeside arrive with the same turbulent mix of emotions that John felt. They are all fearful of what will happen to them, they all swing between shame and anger at needing treatment and they all are locked to a greater or lesser degree in the lonely isolation that addiction ultimately breeds. Also all patients enter treatment with a mix of reasons some external and some internal, for submitting to help.

Our goals for all patients have not changed in the 25 plus years of our existence. Simply put the goals are:

1. To welcome and embrace all patients with respect and empathy while communicating a strong belief in their ability to recover from addiction.

2. To ease the physical and psychological pains of withdrawal from psychoactive drugs.

3. To help each patient understand and accept the nature and consequences of the disease.

4. To provide the tools necessary to sustain lasting recovery after treatment.

5. To help all patients create a detailed recovery plan that addresses the action steps that each must take to avoid relapse and enjoy sobriety.

Everything we do at Lakeside is guided by these goals and everyone in the Lakeside family is committed to emphasizing the best practices to achieve the objectives. At admission, patients are welcomed warmly and made to feel at ease. All patients, unless arriving directly from a detox facility, are monitored for withdrawal symptoms. Some patients in severe withdrawal may be medicated and put on bed rest but most while in detoxification are urged to mix with other patients. Each patient is given a "buddy," a patient who has been in the center for a while, whose job is to orient the new patient to the grounds and the structure of the daily program.

A preliminary medical assessment and blood work charts the physical signs of withdrawal. A full medical assessment with the Nurse Practitioner follows when the lab results return, usually the day after admission. If the patient is suffering physical problems, those problems are addressed. Should any acute physical problems occur during a patient's stay, the patient is immediately brought for treatment to Evergreen Hospital, a short 4-minute drive.

As soon as possible patients are introduced to the fellow members of their color group, those people with whom they will closely walk the path to recovery. Twice a day the group will meet to challenge, encourage and support each other. The challenge is for each member to shed the many defenses (e.g. denial, minimization, rationalization) that enabled the disease to control their lives. Members who may fear life without chemicals are encouraged to understand that sobriety can be rich and rewarding. The group supports each other in helping to shape plans that make recovery the number one priority in life after treatment.

To those who picture addicts as uncaring, pleasure driven creatures it may be surprising that most patients arrive in treatment with a heavy burden of shame and guilt. Once detoxified and forced to look at the damages of life before treatment, many patients fall into an initial despair of ever changing. They view themselves as bad people who have hurt loved ones needlessly and sabotaged their family and work lives. Over the first two weeks of treatment the program and the milieu are structured to teach patients the facts about their disease, most notably that the bad behavior and negative emotions are the natural effects of the progression of addiction. Patients learn to separate themselves from their disease and take a dispassionate look at how a sober life can free them from repeating the mistakes of the past. Shame and guilt are paralyzing while regret, hope and the desire to make amends are energizing.

The patient meets with a counselor who also facilitates the group. Together the patient and counselor sift through the patient's current life to note any problem that must be addressed if the patient is to begin a solid recovery. If the patient is in a problematic relationship or complains of stress as a trigger to drink or use the counselor will draft a treatment plan that will lead to a resolution of the problem during treatment. Some issues will be addressed after intensive treatment in continuing care.

Each day of treatment is highly structured. Addiction robs its victims not only of control over their ability to choose not to drink/use but also over any sense of order in their lives. A daily routine restores a sense of balance and purpose for patients whose only guide has been the constant obsession with drinking and/or using drugs. Interactive lectures and groups twice daily are accompanied by evening sessions that families can attend and in-house or outside 12-step meetings. Time in the afternoon is given for recreation, playing volleyball or basketball or walking the scenic path around the property. Visiting hours are confined to weekends when there are also family communication workshops whose goal is to begin to repair the fractures that have taken place between family members and addicts.

All the information dispensed in lectures and films is processed in the groups that anchor each treatment day. The group is a primary catalyst for learning and change at Lakeside. On any given day some members of the group are asked to challenge their denial system that feeds addiction, while others who have moved into acceptance of their disease are growing the confidence to change their self-defeating behavior and beliefs. The counselor's job is to nudge and nurture the group. Using Rational Emotive Therapy, the counselor teaches the group that all the powerful negative emotions that addiction breeds are products of irrational beliefs about themselves and the disease. If the beliefs are challenged they can be turned into rational beliefs that support recovery.

Knowledge about the disease of addiction is essential to the treatment process at Lakeside. The application of that knowledge to each patient's life is the main task of treatment. Throughout our programs and on each groups room wall, a poster is displayed titled "The Recovery Process." The sign points out each attitudinal phase that an addict must travel through to reach solid recovery. All patients begin in some form of denial. Often it is not until the second or third week of treatment that the group process and constant stream of information on the disease lead the patient to the inescapable admission that "I am an addict." Admittance must then lead to the acceptance of the requisites of recovery and the major life changes that must accompany recovery. Finally in full recovery the addict reaches surrender, a determination to do whatever is necessary to maintain the new sober life.

Throughout the course of treatment patients are asked often to place themselves in the stage of recovery that best mirrors their attitude. Since we are all fallible, changeable human beings it is not unusual for counselors to see patients shifting back and forth between denial and admittance. One of the effects of addiction to alcohol and other drugs in post acute withdrawal is to make a person emotionally "labile," slipping in and out of uncomfortable emotions and a heightened perception of stress.

To confront the twisting emotions, Lakeside employs Rational Emotive Behavior Therapy (RET). The therapy was created in 1955 by Albert Ellis, a psychologist. Borrowing from Greek philosophies, Ellis put forth the proposition that our emotions, especially our strong negative feelings, are not the result of interactions with others (e.g. "you make me mad") but rather the result of unsafe or unnatural beliefs we develop over time (e.g. "I am always right"). In the case of addiction, most addicts develop similar unsafe beliefs that give rise to destructive emotions. Some of the most common fallacies are:
"Being an addict is a measure of my worth." – producing shame
"Things have to go my way." – producing anger, resentment
"My case is different." – producing denial, rationalization

Patients are taught to examine their negative emotions to find the unsafe beliefs and then to challenge those beliefs with reality. New beliefs then form (e.g. "I am not my disease and what I do determines my worth") and patients practice them in treatment.

The group process provides one other benefit for the members. Addiction isolates and estranges its victim. Hiding from friends and loved ones takes a great emotional toll on the addict and he or she learns not to share the shame and guilt they feel. In group, members begin to feel connections with others who have felt the same feelings and hidden themselves away from true human contact. There is a shared humanity that gives rise to a sense of hope and the possibility of a different way of living.

A pivotal point in treatment for each group member is the presentation of a "first step" in front of the entire group. It is an enactment of the first step of Alcoholics Anonymous, "We admitted we were powerless over alcohol – that our lives had become unmanageable." Each patient's revelation of the effects of addiction on their lives is a demonstration of both humility and acceptance. For most, preparation for the first step is painful and humbling. Becoming brutally honest about the ravages of addiction and recounting your losses to a group of people strips away the defenses that shield you from the awful reality of the disease. If a patient minimizes the effects of the disease, fellow group members are quick to point out the missing parts of the story. Conversely, if a patient seems devoid of self-esteem in relating his or her first step, fellow patients are quick to remind the presenter of the courage displayed in an honest first step.

In the last week of treatment patients are asked to make careful plans for reentering into the world they left before treatment. How are you going to build on the information and skills learned during your treatment? What recovery activities will you build into each day in your life after treatment? What are the high-risk situations and people that you have to avoid at all costs to prevent relapse? What negative emotions do you have to deal with and how will you negate their ability to lead you into relapse? How will you deal with stress differently? These are the questions each patient has to answer, and their responses constitute a careful recovery plan that must be followed to ensure ongoing sobriety.

Following treatment the patient can relay their progress and discuss new problems that may arise at continuing care sessions. For some patients who are still struggling at discharge, counselors may recommend attending an intensive outpatient program. For others worried about the return of relapse triggers, there is the Renewal Program, a weekly session that is coupled with continuing care to provide another safeguard for sobriety.

Treatment is a difficult, often painful and finally a rewarding journey. We at Lakeside continue to learn from our patients as they learn from us.

The Place of Spirituality

"Spirituality is the amalgam of the positive emotions that bind us to other human beings – and to our experience of God as we may understand him/her" (George Vaillant, Spiritual Evolution). The reawakening of the addict's spirit is essential to dispel the awful isolation which is at the very heart of active addiction. The rise of the spirit also mitigates the negative emotions that pervade the drinking/using life – fear, anger, shame and guilt. In their place the awakened spirit can begin to feel love, hope, joy, compassion, faith and gratitude.

Each morning at the inpatient center opens with a group reading – a brief meditation on those values that we ask patients to practice each day. An orientation to meditation is offered each morning for 45 minutes because meditation has been found not only to offer physical benefits like reduced muscle tension and blood pressure, but also to induce positive emotions in the "parasympathetic" nervous system. Researchers are finding that just as there is part of the brain responsible for addiction, there is another part of the brain that has evolved to access the spiritual ties that bind families and communities together.

Alcoholics Anonymous is a spiritual program. The founders of Alcoholics Anonymous came to the conclusion that unless the alcoholic could admit powerlessness over the addiction, he or she would forever engage in a losing battle with the disease. In one sense, AA is a program that encourages giving up the battle by surrendering willpower and accepting help from another source. The practice of the AA program awakens and enlarges the spirit of each member and reengages the sense of community and service to others.

The reawakening of the spirit comes quickly to some patients and emerges slowly for others. Whenever it occurs, there is a remarkable transformation that is evident to staff and other patients. Patients speak simply and clearly about how differently they feel toward the future and a new emotion – hope.

The Importance of 12-Step Programs

Alcoholics Anonymous (AA) began as the meeting between two men who had been labeled hopeless drunks. Bill Wilson, a former successful stockbroker, had all but despaired of even becoming sober. After many episodes of detox, he had contact with the Oxford Groups, a group of mostly non-alcoholics that emphasized fellowship and spiritual values. He was not drinking but increasingly afraid of relapsing when he was introduced in 1935 to Dr. Bob Smith, a local surgeon who was also trying to apply Oxford Group principles to get sober. They sat and shared their personal histories and found a release from the urge to drink. Bill used the information he learned from Dr. William Silkworth, a physician in a New York Hospital who emphasized that alcoholism was a disease that affected the body, mind and spirit. Together Bill and Dr. Bob began meeting other alcoholics in Akron, Ohio and shared the belief that sobriety could be acquired "one day at a time."

The organization, self-supporting and self-governing,

grew slowly. In 1939 Bill wrote Alcoholics Anonymous, forever known as the Big Book, which explained how AA worked and included the group's Twelve Steps to recovery. Membership grew exponentially over the next 10 years with meetings started all over the world. AA remains self-supporting and still maintains that "there are no dues or fees. The only requirement for membership is a desire to quit drinking."

At last count in 2008 AA counted over 2,000,000 members worldwide in over 116,000 groups. In cities there are AA meetings every day of the week and around the clock. There are few places in the world where an AA member can go and not find a meeting and a group of fellow recovering people.

As late as 30 years ago researchers in the field dismissed AA as a quasi-religious sect with little value for victims of alcoholism/addiction. In the last 10 years however, there have been a host of studies that attempt to explain the success of AA in fostering recovery. Patient surveys, including our own, have demonstrated again and again that the most successful outcomes and lengths of sobriety are achieved by those who leave treatment and become members of AA or one of the other established 12-Step Programs, like Narcotics Anonymous (NA).

12-Step Programs are not religious organizations, but they do espouse a spiritual regimen. The 12 steps lead a member from acknowledging powerlessness over alcohol and/or other drugs to a belief in a Higher Power defined by the individual, to working on the defects that may lead to relapse and then sharing what they've learned with others. In the process the AA member gains what one researcher labeled a "quantum change," an enduring personal transformation. By its singular focus on sobriety, AA becomes a constant harbor for the alcoholic from the pressures and triggers that might otherwise overwhelm a newly recovering person. In helping other alcoholics the recovering alcoholic moves away from the spiritual vacuum of the disease of alcoholism as Bill Wilson saw it – "self-will run riot."

A Plan for Recovery

While each patient leaves inpatient treatment at LMRC with an individualized recovery plan, all patients leave with the following recommendations:

1. Attend 90 12-step meetings in the first 90 days after discharge,
2. Find a 12-step sponsor with whom to work the program, and
3. Become an active member of a 12-step program with a home group (a weekly meeting always attended and a willingness to do service work (e.g., set up meetings, make coffee, reach out to other alcoholics in need).

AA and other 12-step programs have proven unequivocally to be the best long-term support for lasting recovery from addiction.

John and His Treatment

John wanted nothing more than to be left alone when he entered Lakeside. Instead he was surrounded by people – the Associate Counselors who oriented him to the facility, the nurse who did a medical assessment, his assigned buddy, and very shortly the other members of his group. He was given some reading and assignments for the first week of his stay. John found everyone nice enough but he was quiet and still angry about ending up in treatment. He went to bed the first night still fearful of what to expect.

The first week passed in a kind of blur. The nurse practitioner found no problems with his lab work or her assessment of his physical condition. He went to all the activities, remained as quiet as he was allowed and found he was tired at the end of each day. He liked one guy in his group and spent time talking to him and sharing little by little how they both arrived at Lakeside. George was entering his last week and made it clear that he belonged in treatment and was determined to stay sober when he left. George had been sober for a year when he gradually stopped going to meetings thinking he didn't need them. After a bad fight with his wife he had found himself in a bar and started drinking again. He woke up in 2 weeks with the realization that he couldn't live as a drunk anymore. He shared what he learned with John.

When John talked to Maureen on the phone she encouraged him and repeated that he was doing the right thing. He still believed he didn't belong in treatment; Maureen disagreed strongly.

John's main roadblock to really engaging in treatment was minimization. As he began to open up in group he would assert that things really weren't that bad. The counselor and later his fellow group members reminded him that things were indeed bad and social drinkers didn't disappear for 2 days, get DUI's and drink alone in bars.

John attended AA meetings and found to his surprise that they weren't full of "holy rollers" who spouted religion at him. They were folks not unlike himself who were trying to stay sober by working a program. John began reading the Big Book of Alcoholics Anonymous and started to see the similarities between his drinking and that described in the book. On his 15th day in treatment John haltingly shared in group that he thought maybe he did belong in treatment. He had moved from denial to the admission of his disease and somehow he began to feel relieved. He took part in his group's discussions more actively and found that he could spot the same defenses he used in other group members. Besides George, he began to feel very connected to other group members.

Maureen wrote an "effects letter" which his counselor asked John to read in the group. For the first time in years John found himself crying as he realized the toll that his disease had taken not only on his wife, but also his kids. That night he wrote his wife a letter apologizing for what he had done and promising to somehow make it right when he left treatment.

During the next week John experienced strange mood swings, becoming confident and engaged one day and falling into a depression the next day. His counselor reminded John that mood swings were a symptom of post acute withdrawal and that his mood would stabilize as he became immersed in his program of recovery. On the day he was to give his First Step in group John felt withdrawn and fearful. As he recounted his powerlessness over alcohol and other drugs he began to feel, again, the connection with his fellow group members and his fear left him. "Maybe," he thought, "this is what a spiritual awakening is."

In his last days in treatment his counselor congratulated John on his hard work during treatment, but also cautioned him, "This part is only the beginning of your work. You're going back to a world that hasn't changed. You need to have a plan to deal with the stresses at work, the family's needs and work on your own program." John created a recovery plan that focused on what AA meetings he would commit to attending as well as listing the tools he would use to avoid getting overwhelmed at work. He made a commitment to becoming part of the family life that had fractured during his addiction.

In one way John left treatment as he entered – he was a little frightened of his reentry into everyday life. He called his new sponsor as soon as he arrived home and planned the rest of his day to end with a meeting. He decided that the AA slogan was indeed true – one day at a time you could stay sober.

Who Recovers, Who Relapses?

Addiction has been classified as a chronic disease, in other words a persistent illness that can reoccur. This is not news to AA members who have for years summarized the condition with a metaphor – "you can't change a pickle back to a cucumber." Unlike some other chronic diseases which can reoccur and for which there is no known medical resolution, addiction is a disease from which victims can and do recover if they follow a prescribed regimen that supports recovery.

For years the public attitude toward alcoholics and other drug addicts was pessimistic – "they simply don't get better." The reality is that treated addicts relapse at about the same or lower rates than of victims of other chronic diseases like diabetes and hypertension. Data from the National Center of Health Statistics reveal that less than 50% of diagnosed adult diabetics adhere to the prescribed medication regimen and as many as 50% of those patients need to be retreated within 12 months. Fifty to sixty percent of hypertensive patients are retreated within 12 months with less than 35% adhering to the prescribed regimen of diet and exercise. Most national outcome studies of addiction treatment cite that between 50-60% of diagnosed and treated addicts remain sober for 12 months following treatment.

At Lakeside we have conducted outcome studies for 20 years. Our first study was conducted by an independent organization specializing in follow-up protocols. In that study 67% of discharged patients reported being abstinent from psychoactive drugs when contacted one year after treatment. Subsequent outcome reports taken 3 months after treatment have replicated those numbers with between 60 and 70 percent of reporting patients confirming their abstinence.

Why do addicts relapse? The simplest answer was given over 60 years ago by Dr. William Silkworth, a physician who directed the addiction treatment program at Towns Hospital in New York City. Dr. Silkworth, who had a profound effect on Bill Wilson, cofounder of AA, wrote a paper in which he compared the disease of addiction to cardiac disease and tuberculosis. In all cases, "the patient didn't follow directions. And that's human nature! It's life! It's happening all the time, not merely among alcoholics, but among all kinds of people. The preventive is plain. The patient must have full knowledge of his condition, keep in mind the facts of his case and the nature of his disease, and follow orders."

Some patients don't follow directions and that is why relapse occurs. In our studies somewhere between 13 and 20% of discharged inpatients suffer relapse in the first ninety days after treatment. Those same patients confess that they went to only one or two 12-step meetings and one or two continuing care sessions at Lakeside. They were swept up in the same stresses, the same triggers to drink and use that plagued them before treatment with no defenses to hold them at bay. We find that the most common triggers for relapse are the following:

1. Repeating old behaviors – an alcoholic believes he can return to his favorite bar and drink club soda while watching a football game. The teenager believes he can still

hang out with his using friends and stay sober. Recovery requires elements of changes in behavior because the brain records all the people, places and attitudes that were triggers to drink/use.

2. Not practicing new behaviors – we have a saying that "recovery is like an escalator – if you're not moving forward you're slipping back." Patients who leave treatment and believe that the work and skills taught in treatment really aren't necessary in their lives are those most likely to relapse. Becoming active in a 12-step program, using RET to deal with the turbulent emotions of early recovery, developing a strong recovery network – these are behaviors that need to be practiced daily so that the brain can establish the triggers for sobriety.

3. Forgetting or not believing that <u>all</u> psychoactive substances are toxic to the addict's brain. The neurotransmission system of the addict will always mal-function when psychoactive drugs are ingested. The addicted person who believes that marijuana isn't addictive has decided to relapse. The brain will

immediately begin the craving cycle that demands more of the substance in order to feel "normal."

Special mention must be made of psychoactive prescription and over the counter drugs that cause the same dysfunction. A list of commonly prescribed and over the counter medications that are dangerous is included in the inpatient manual given to every patient.

When surgery requires painkillers like opioids to relieve the acute pain of post surgery, the addict must limit their use to the shortest possible duration and let another trusted 12-step member or family member hold the drugs and administer only what is prescribed. It is not unusual that physicians will prescribe much more of a drug than is necessary so the addict must monitor pain and step down to non narcotic alternatives as soon as possible. A drug specialist or pharmacist should be consulted if the addict is not sure of the nature of any prescribed drug.

The good news is that most of these patients after the relapse realized that the disease couldn't be arrested with good intentions. Recovery is a program of action not intention. Those who enter into continuous sobriety place their recovery first in their daily lives and do what has been prescribed in their discharge summaries – become actively involved in a 12-step group, attend continuing care and surround themselves with a solid support system – 12-step meeting friends, sponsors and loving, non-addicted family members. They use all the tools available to manage stress, avoid high-risk situations and challenge the negative emotions that may arise.

The very best announcement a family can receive from a patient arriving home from treatment is, "I need to put all my energy into staying sober."

Recovering After Relapse

From a number of outcome studies of addicts after treatment there are clear patterns of the lives of addicts after relapse. About a third of these relapsing patients stick to the prescription of recovery for a time and then begin to believe they do not need further support. Old habits reemerge insidiously in four to six months and the relapse process moves into drinking/using again. These addicts are fortunate, however, because they initially use the tools of recovery after treatment and found success. Their relapses are short-lived because they call sponsors, return to 12-step meetings and go back to treatment when necessary.

Another third of patients are not so fortunate. They leave treatment, return to high risk environments and are quickly caught up in stress and anxiety. They make few changes in their lives, but they are stunned when they find themselves deep in relapse. They may return to treatment again and again until they understand the power of the disease and the near impossibility of achieving recovery until they surrender and use the supports available to them.

The final third of patients should really not be called relapsers. For whatever reason they entered treatment, but were unable to recognize the disease in themselves despite the best efforts of professionals, fellow patients, and members of 12-step programs. They return to drinking and / or using upon leaving treatment. In many cases long-term treatment (i.e., a year or more) is needed in a safe environment to open their hearts and minds to the possibility of recovery.

There is Always Hope

If there is one attitude that is shared with each patient from the time they walk through the front door of the treatment center till the time of discharge, it is hope. The message of each lecture, the closing of each group is a reminder that recovery is possible and indeed probable when the path of recovery is followed. The patient who relapses remembers all those other staff and patients who found sobriety after facing the same obstacles.

"You cannot study hope objectively or even rationally. Nor can you quantify the beauty of butterflies' lives or the grace of five-year-old children yet all are real. Perhaps of more importance, hope saves lives" (George Vaillant, Spiritual Evolution). Hope opens the door to the possibility of recovery which eventually becomes faith and trust in the means to recovery. It begins in the pains of detox with voices of all staff assuring each patient that, "This Too Shall Pass." It continues with the hope in twelve step programs that a power greater than themselves may restore them to sanity. Once ignited hope is never fully extinguished for the addict who can remember the 28 days of abstinence and the lessons and experience learned in the programs. There is in our philosophy no such thing as a "hopeless addict."

How Prevalent are Co-Occurring Disorders?

When used today, the term "co-occurring disorder" refers to the simultaneous presence of addiction and a mental health disorder (e.g., depression, anxiety, panic disorder). There are widely divergent estimates about the prevalence of co-occurring disorders among addicts with some reports alleging that as many as 75% of adult addicts and an even higher percentage of adolescent addicts are victims of co-occurring disorders.

It is our experience at LMRC that it is quite true that many patients arrive in treatment for addiction exhibiting depression, anxiety and other mood disorders. We find however that those conditions, rather than being co-existing separately defined maladies, are the result of the prolonged use of psychoactive substances. Alcohol is a sedative drug and as such depresses the central nervous system and impairs the neurotransmission system of the brain. Prolonged addictive use causes a depressed feeling state that with abstinence and a program of recovery usually resolves itself in a month to 6 months. In one study,

72% of the male alcoholics reported that (Peratis et al, 2002) alcohol addiction <u>preceded</u> the onset of a mood disorder. Stimulant addicts also report a great deal of anxiety in withdrawal that may continue in a post acute withdrawal phase. In all these cases the disorders appear to be caused by the disruption in the limbic reward system of the brain and the lack of production of certain neurotransmitters (dopamine, serotonin, etc). The brain has an amazing ability to "reset" itself and with time return normal functioning to the neurotransmission system.

Teenagers present a special problem in the diagnosis of co-occurring disorders. The frontal cortex is the part of the brain that acts as a "brake" on the mesolimbic reward system and the eventual progression of chemical addiction. In the early stages of the disease the adult victim may be able to override the impulse to drink/use more by employing the rationality that resides in the prefrontal area of the brain. The prefrontal cortex however does not fully develop in humans for 20-25 years. Teenage addicts thus have a limited ability to make wise and safe decisions when alcohol and drugs are ingested. Flagrant mood

swings and risky behavior are the norms for teenagers trapped in addiction and may easily be misdiagnosed as mental health disorders.

In the diagnosis of addicts suspecting of having a co-occurring disorder, one central question must always be posed, "When did the alleged mood disorder begin?" If the maladaptive behavior began after the child began drinking and using drugs, the chances are great that a substance-induced state is present. The chances are also great that the "disorder" will abate with a commitment to abstinence and structured recovery.

At LMRC, less that 6% of admitted patients are found to be suffering from co-occurring mental health disorders needing concurrent mental health treatment.

For Further Reading

Under the Influence. James Milam, PhD and Katherine Ketcham, Bantam Books, 1981. Dr. Milam's landmark explanation of the nature of alcoholism.

Your Drug May Be Your Problem. Peter Breggin, MD and David Cohen, PhD. Lifelong Books, 2007. An examination of the dangers of prescribed psychoactive drugs.

Spiritual Evolution, How We are Wired for Faith, Hope and Love. George E. Vaillant, MD. Broadway Books, 2008. Dr. Vaillant, a creator of long-term outcome studies of alcoholics, traces the roots of man's spirituality to the evolution of the brain.

The books are available at amazon.com